Flute

INSTRUMENTAL PLAY-ALONG

POP HITS

SOLO ARRANGEMENTS OF 15 GREAT POP SONGS WITH CD ACCOMPANIMENT

HOW TO USE THE CD ACCOMPANIMENT:

A melody cue appears on the right channel only.

If your CD player has a balance adjustment, you can adjust the volume of the melody by turning down the right channel.

This publication is not authorised for sale in the United States of America and/or Canada

HAL LEONARD EUROPE

DISTRIBUTED BY MUSIC SALES

Exclusive Distributors:
Music Sales Limited
14-15 Berners Street, London W1T 3LJ, UK.

Order No. HLE90003430
ISBN: 978-1-84772-517-2
This book © Copyright 2008 Hal Leonard Europe

Unauthorised reproduction of any part of this publication by any means including photocopying is an infringement of copyright.

Printed in the USA

Your Guarantee of Quality
As publishers, we strive to produce every book to the highest commercial standards. The book has been carefully designed to minimise awkward page turns and to make playing from it a real pleasure. Throughout, the printing and binding have been planned to ensure a sturdy, attractive publication which should give years of enjoyment. If your copy fails to meet our high standards, please inform us and we will gladly replace it.

www.musicsales.com

Contents

BLACK HORSE AND THE CHERRY TREE

FLUTE

Words and Music by
KATIE TUNSTALL

Copyright © 2004 Sony/ATV Music Publishing UK Ltd.
All Rights Administered by Sony/ATV Music Publishing, 8 Music Square West, Nashville, TN 37203
International Copyright Secured All Rights Reserved

D.S. al Coda
CODA

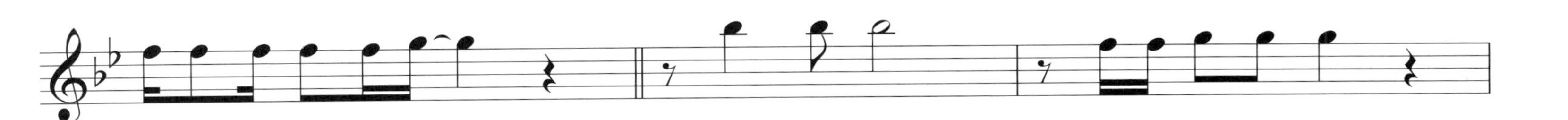

❷ CRAZY

FLUTE

Words and Music by BRIAN BURTON,
THOMAS CALLAWAY, GIANPIERO REVERBERI
and GIANFRANCO REVERBERI

Copyright © 2006 Chrysalis Music Ltd., Warner/Chappell Music Publishing Ltd. and BMG Ricordi Music Publishing SpA
All Rights for Chrysalis Music Ltd. in the U.S. and Canada Administered by Chrysalis Music
All Rights for Warner/Chappell Music Publishing Ltd. in the U.S. and Canada Administered by Warner-Tamerlane Publishing Corp.
All Rights for BMG Ricordi Music Publishing SpA in the U.S. and Canada Administered by Killer Tracks
All Rights Reserved Used by Permission
- contains a sample of "Last Men Standing" by GianPiero Reverberi and GianFranco Reverberi

EVERYTHING

FLUTE

Words and Music by
ALANIS MORISSETTE

Copyright © 2002 by Szeretlek
All Rights for the World Administered by BMG Music Publishing International Ltd.
All Rights for the U.S. Administered by BMG Songs, Inc.
International Copyright Secured All Rights Reserved

5 THE FIRST CUT IS THE DEEPEST

FLUTE

Words and Music by
CAT STEVENS

Moderately

Guitar

Play

mf

To Coda

1.

2.

3

D.S. al Coda

CODA

Copyright © 1967 SALAFA LTD.
Copyright Renewed
All Rights in the U.S. and Canada Controlled and Administered by UNIVERSAL MUSIC CORP.
All Rights Reserved Used by Permission

4 FALLEN

FLUTE

Words and Music by
SARAH McLACHLAN

Copyright © 2003 Sony/ATV Songs LLC and Tyde Music
All Rights Administered by Sony/ATV Music Publishing, 8 Music Square West, Nashville, TN 37203
International Copyright Secured All Rights Reserved

3
4

6 HEY YA!

FLUTE

Words and Music by
ANDRE BENJAMIN

Copyright © 2003 Chrysalis Music and Gnat Booty Music
All Rights Administered by Chrysalis Music
All Rights Reserved Used by Permission

1.
2.
2

7 IT'S MY LIFE

FLUTE

Words and Music by MARK DAVID HOLLIS
and TIM FRIESE-GREENE

Copyright © 1984 HOLLIS SONGS LTD. and ZOMBA MUSIC PUBLISHING LTD.
All Rights for HOLLIS SONGS LTD. in the U.S. and Canada Controlled and Administered by UNIVERSAL - SONGS OF POLYGRAM INTERNATIONAL, INC.
All Rights Reserved Used by Permission

To Coda
4
mf
3
D.S. al Coda
CODA
1.
2.

8 LISTEN

from the Motion Picture DREAMGIRLS

FLUTE

Words and Music by HENRY KRIEGER, ANNE PREVEN,
SCOTT CUTLER and BEYONCÉ KNOWLES

Copyright © 2006 Miroku Music, EMI April Music Inc., B-Day Publishing, Scottarock Music, SKG Songs, Shigshag Music, Songs Of SKG and Kobalt Music Publishing Ltd.
All Rights for Miroku Music Administered by Williamson Music
All Rights for B-Day Publishing Controlled and Administered by EMI April Music Inc.
All Rights for SKG Songs in the United States and Canada Administered by Cherry Lane Music Publishing Company, Inc.
All Rights for Songs Of SKG in the United States and Canada Administered by Cherry River Music Co.
International Copyright Secured All Rights Reserved

D.S. al Coda
(take 2nd ending)
CODA
3
3
3

9 MOVE ALONG

FLUTE

Words and Music by TYSON RITTER and NICK WHEELER

Copyright © 2005 by BMG Songs, Inc. and Smells Like Phys Ed Music
All Rights in the U.S. Administered by BMG Songs
International Copyright Secured All Rights Reserved

mp–f
2
Play 4 times

10 TAKE MY BREATH AWAY
(Love Theme)

from the Paramount Picture TOP GUN

FLUTE

Words and Music by GIORGIO MORODER
and TOM WHITLOCK

Copyright © 1986 by Famous Music Corporation and Budde Music, Inc.
All Rights on behalf of Budde Music, Inc. Administered by WB Music Corp.
International Copyright Secured All Rights Reserved

13 WHITE FLAG

FLUTE

Words and Music by RICK NOWELS, ROLLO ARMSTRONG and DIDO ARMSTRONG

© 2003 EMI APRIL MUSIC INC., FUTURE FURNITURE MUSIC, BMG MUSIC PUBLISHING LTD. and WARNER/CHAPPELL MUSIC LTD.
All Rights for FUTURE FURNITURE MUSIC Controlled and Administered by EMI APRIL MUSIC INC.
All Rights for BMG MUSIC PUBLISHING LTD. in the U.S. Controlled and Administered by BMG SONGS, INC.
All Rights for WARNER/CHAPPELL MUSIC LTD. Controlled and Administered by WB MUSIC CORP.
All Rights Reserved International Copyright Secured Used by Permission

11 UNFAITHFUL

FLUTE

Words and Music by MIKKEL ERIKSEN,
TOR ERIK HERMANSEN and SHAFFER SMITH

© 2006 EMI MUSIC PUBLISHING LTD., SONY/ATV MUSIC PUBLISHING UK LTD., ZOMBA SONGS and SUPER SAYIN PUBLISHING
All Rights for EMI MUSIC PUBLISHING LTD. in the U.S. and Canada Controlled and Administered by EMI APRIL MUSIC INC.
All Rights for SONY/ATV MUSIC PUBLISHING UK LTD. Administered by SONY/ATV MUSIC PUBLISHING, 8 Music Square West, Nashville, TN 37203
All Rights for SUPER SAYIN PUBLISHING Administered by ZOMBA SONGS
All Rights Reserved International Copyright Secured Used by Permission

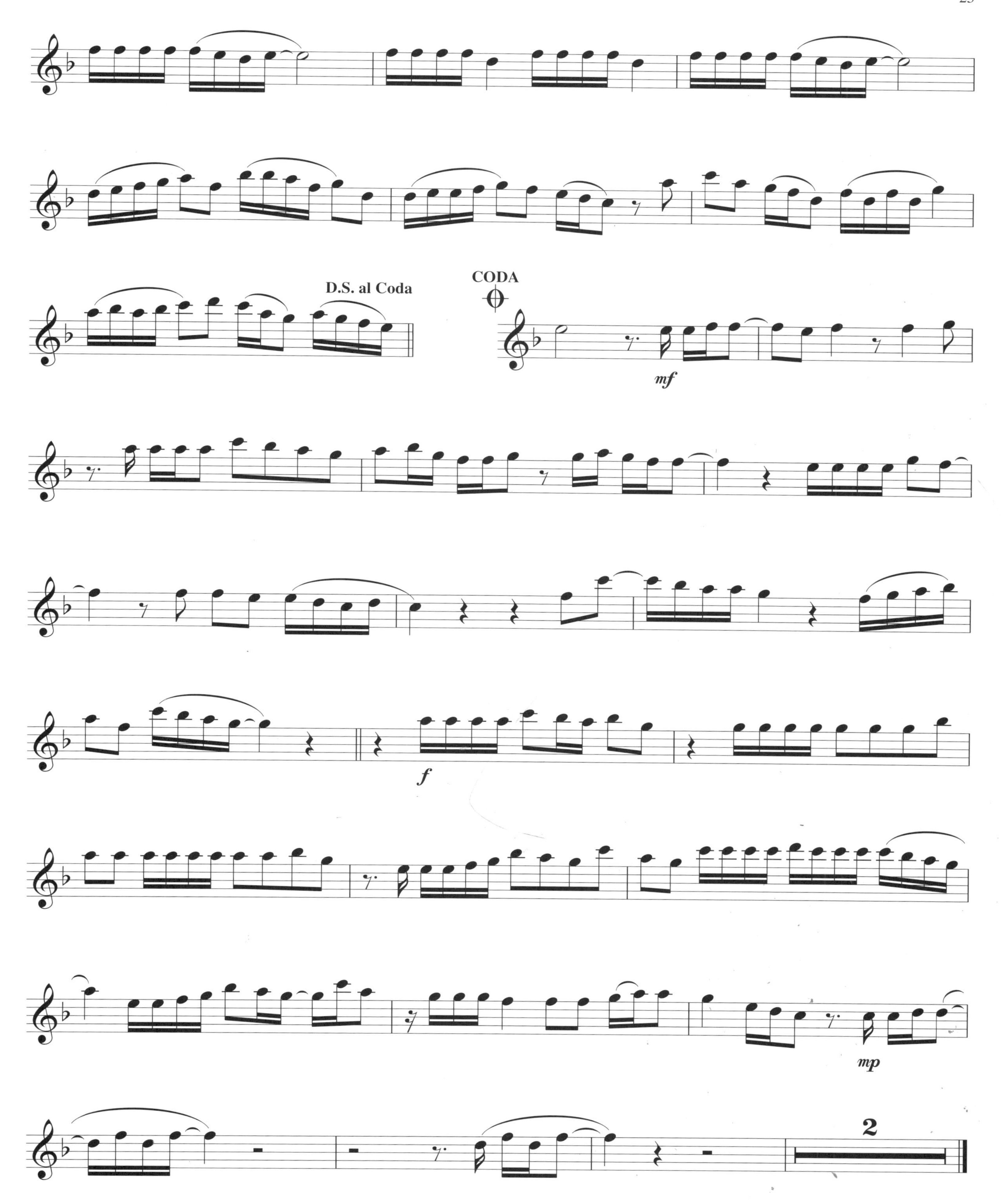
D.S. al Coda
CODA
mf
f
mp
2

12 UNWRITTEN

FLUTE

Words and Music by NATASHA BEDINGFIELD,
DANIELLE BRISEBOIS and WAYNE RODRIGUES

© 2004 EMI MUSIC PUBLISHING LTD., EMI BLACKWOOD MUSIC INC., GATOR BABY and WSRJ MUSIC
All Rights for EMI MUSIC PUBLISHING LTD. in the U.S. and Canada Controlled and Administered by EMI BLACKWOOD MUSIC INC.
All Rights for GATOR BABY Controlled and Administered by EMI BLACKWOOD MUSIC INC.
All Rights Reserved International Copyright Secured Used by Permission

1.
3
2.
f
To Coda
3
mf
D.S. al Coda
CODA

YOU'RE BEAUTIFUL

FLUTE

Words and Music by JAMES BLUNT,
SACHA SCARBECK and AMANDA GHOST

© 2005 EMI MUSIC PUBLISHING LTD., UNIVERSAL MUSIC PUBLISHING LTD. and BUCKS MUSIC LTD.
All Rights for EMI MUSIC PUBLISHING LTD. in the U.S. and Canada Controlled and Administered by EMI BLACKWOOD MUSIC INC.
All Rights for UNIVERSAL MUSIC PUBLISHING LTD. in the U.S. and Canada Controlled and Administered by
UNIVERSAL - SONGS OF POLYGRAM INTERNATIONAL, INC.
All Rights for BUCKS MUSIC LTD. in the U.S. Administered by DAVID PLATZ MUSIC (USA) INC.
All Rights Reserved International Copyright Secured Used by Permission

2

D.S. al Coda

CODA

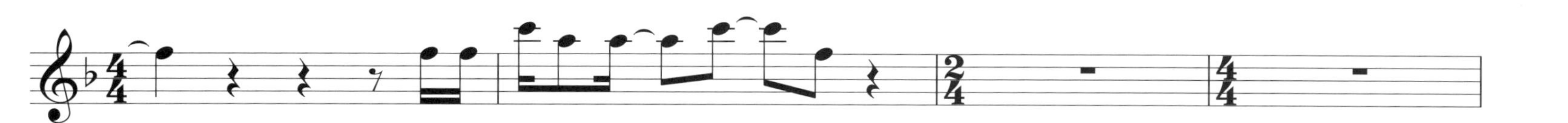

14 YOU RAISE ME UP

FLUTE

Words and Music by BRENDAN GRAHAM
and ROLF LOVLAND

Copyright © 2002 by Peermusic (Ireland) Ltd. and Universal Music Publishing, A Division of Universal Music AS
All Rights for Universal Music Publishing, A Division of Universal Music AS Controlled and Administered in the U.S. and Canada by
Universal - PolyGram International Publishing, Inc.
International Copyright Secured All Rights Reserved